Character of the Christian

BOOK FOUR

Studies in Christian Living

NAVPRESS

A MINISTRY OF THE NAVIGATORS

Post Office Box 20, Colorado Springs, Colorado 80901

The Navigators is an international, evangelical
Christian organization. Jesus Christ gave His
followers the Great Commission to go and make
disciples (Matthew 28:19). The aim of The
Navigators is to help fulfill that commission by
multiplying laborers for Christ in every nation.

NavPress is the publishing ministry of The
Navigators. NavPress publications are tools to
help Christians grow. Although publications alone
cannot make disciples or change lives, they can
help believers learn biblical discipleship, and apply
what they learn to their lives and ministries.

Thirty-second printing, 1980

Printed in the United States of America

At Milepost Four

If you have completed Books 1, 2 and 3 of *Studies In Christian Living*, you already know the profit of personal Bible study . . . what it means to search the Scriptures and come up with answers. You have probably noticed how the Word you have quarried out for yourself has affected your attitudes and actions day by day.

But even though you believe in systematic Bible study, it's likely you will sense opposition as you continue it. And there's a reason. The enemy of every Christian, Satan himself, knows the power of God's Word in your life and he will try at every turn to keep you from it. He will suggest such excuses as, "You're too busy". . ."You can't concentrate now—do this little thing first, then get to Bible study." He will engineer interruptions, temptations and even criticism by others to hinder you from giving your attention to the Word of God.

Just recognizing that Satan is the source of such hindrances is helpful. It re-emphasizes the importance of Bible study, and can spur your determination to gain victory.

How to win? Here are some suggestions:

First, accept by faith the victory that Christ has already won over Satan and all his works. "*But thanks be to God, which giveth us the victory through our Lord Jesus Christ*" (I Corinthians 15:57).

Second, seek the Lord's wisdom and strength.

Third, use personal discipline. No spiritual exercise becomes automatic. Just as you have to make an effort to keep up your daily time with the Lord, so you must plan and zealously guard your study time. It's good to set a definite goal for a certain amount of study to be completed each week, and be diligent in reaching that goal. "*The desire accomplished is sweet to the soul* . . ." states Proverbs 13:19, and a certain satisfaction is yours when you reach a given objective as planned.

Fourth, arrange with a friend to check each other weekly on completed goals in Bible study . . . and perhaps share something you received from it.

This fourth book concerns what you as a Christian should aspire to *be* in Christ. It deals with the basis of Christian character—the life of Christ in us; virtues expected in the Christian's life; and how to discover God's will. Its five chapters are . . .

- Maturing in Christ
- Demonstrating Christ
- Developing Integrity
- Growing in Discipleship
- Obedience and Blessing

Chapter One

Maturing in Christ

"You will not become perfect in the twinkling of an eye. You can become a Christian in a moment, but not a mature Christian. Christ can enter, and cleanse and forgive you, in a matter of seconds, but it may take a lifetime for your character to be transformed and moulded to His will."
—*John R. W. Stott**

OUR NEW WALK

1   For what purposes has God called us?

(1) Eph. 1:4_____

_____

(2) Rom. 8:29_____

_____

(3) I Pet. 2:9_____

_____

2   I John 2:6 says that believers should (Underline correct answers.)

(1) Live the best lives they can.

(2) Live as Christ lived.

(3) Abide in Christ and avoid any unnecessary contact with the world.

3   What should this new walk be like?

(1) Eph. 5:1, 2_____

_____

(2) Eph. 5:8_____

*Basic Christianity, Wm. B. Eerdmans Publishing Co.

(3) Eph. 4:1_____

(4) Gal. 5:16_____

_____

4 Where should our attention be fixed?

(1) Col. 3:2_____

(2) II Cor. 4:18_____

Also review your study on "The New Life" in **Book 2** which introduces some of these subjects.

HOW WE'RE CHANGED

5 In Philippians 2:13

(1) Who is at work in us?_____

(2) What does He do?_____

_____

6 Consider II Corinthians 3:18

(1) Into Whose image are we changed?_____

(2) Who brings about this change?_____

(3) Are we completely changed all at once?_____

(4) What is our part in this?_____

(5) How do you think we behold His glory?_____

_____

7 In Romans 12:2

(1) What should we avoid?_____

_____

(2) What should be happening to our minds?_____

_____

(3) What are we then able to do?_____

_____

8 In Ephesians 4:22-24

(1) How is our new nature's likeness to God described?_____

_____

_____

(2) What should be our relationship to our old nature and to our new

nature?_____

_____

_____

> When we were brought to spiritual birth by the Holy Spirit, He came to live in us and gave us a new nature. But we still have our old nature with its sinful desires and habits. Our responsibility is to feed and develop the new nature and to starve and deny the old, in order to be pleasing and useful to the Lord.

9 Romans 13:13, 14 give some clear standards on not yielding to sin. Write out these verses in your own words. (Use the definitions page and a dictionary to look up words you don't know.)

_____

_____

_____

_____

_____

_____

_____

_____

10 In Romans 6:11-13

(1) What should you count as true about yourself?_____

_____

_____

(2) What should be our relationship to sin? (verse 12)_____

_____

_____

(3) What must we not allow? (verse 13)_____

_____

_____

(4) What are we to do with ourselves? _____

_____

_____

The context (Romans 6:6-18) of this passage is important and somewhat difficult. You will profit by reading it several times and meditating on it.

11 How can we live this new life? (II Cor. 5:7; Heb. 10:38) (Underline correct answer.)

(1) By confidence in our own abilities.

(2) By sincerity and diligence.

(3) By trust and dependence on Him.

(4) By being clear and certain about major Bible doctrines.

THE LIFE OF FAITH

12 What is a basic requirement for pleasing God? (Heb. 11:6) _____

_____

13 How does one *begin* the Christian life? (Eph. 2:8, 9; Rom. 4:5) ____

_____

14 What is essential as we *continue* in the Christian life? (Col. 2:6, 7)

_____

_____

_____

15 What did Abraham's faith enable him to avoid? (Rom. 4:20)_____

_____

16 How would you define faith from:

(1) Rom. 4:21 _____

_____

(2) Acts 27:25 _____

_____

(3) Heb. 11:1 _____

_____

_____

> "Faith is not a matter of impressions, nor of probabilities, nor of appearances. Faith is the assurance that what God has said in His Word is true, and that God will act according to what He has said in His Word . . ."   —George Muller*

17 What does faith make possible?

(1) Eph. 3:12 _____

_____

(2) Rom. 15:13 _____

_____

(3) Matt. 21:22 _____

_____

*George Muller, Man of Faith, Moody Press

18 What part does faith play in maintaining victory over the enemy?

(1) Eph. 6:16 _____

_____

(2) I Pet. 5:8, 9 _____

19 What are some areas of life in which we should exercise faith? (Matt. 6:25-30) _____

_____

20 What can shipwreck your faith? (I Tim. 1:19) (Underline best answer.)

(1) Lack of understanding.

(2) Ignoring your conscience.

(3) Not listening to the advice of others.

21 From James 1:2-4

(1) How should we react to trials? _____

(2) Why does God allow them? _____

_____

> *"Difficulties, limitations, hindrances, bereavements and losses, though we shrink exceedingly from them, are the very agencies that God uses to cause us to grow. As an infant has its limbs developed by means of exercise and nourishment...so, in a spiritual sense is the Christian made strong by adversity."—George Muller*

22 What godly characteristics accompany mature faith? (I Tim. 6:11)

_____

_____

23 Write out Psalm 37:5 in your own words. _____

_____

_____

24 Read through Hebrews 11 and record the number of times the word "faith" is used and how many things were accomplished by faith.

_____

Which of these do you consider the most remarkable? _____

_____

_____

_____

25 Which are your one or two favorite verses in this chapter? _____

_____

What is the Lord speaking to you about in these verses? _____

_____

_____

_____

_____

_____

_____

Chapter Two

Demonstrating Christ

LOVE IN ACTION

"To love the whole world
For me is no chore;
My only real problem's
My neighbor next door."

1 How is love described? (Rom. 13:10) _____

_____

2 What are the characteristics of genuine love? (I Cor. 13:4-7)* _____

_____

_____

_____

_____

_____

_____

_____

"Faults are thick when love is thin."

3 What things are useless without love? (I Cor. 13:1-3) _____

*Love is translated "charity" in many New Testaments.

_____

_____

_____

_____

The two great chapters on love are I Corinthians 13 and I John 4.

4 What is the surest evidence that we are followers of Christ? (John 13:34, 35) (Underline correct answer.)

(1) Our ability to speak forcefully for Christ.

(2) Our zeal and self-sacrificing church work.

(3) Our love toward other Christians.

(4) Our diligence and fruit in witnessing.

5 What are some commands about love?

(1) I John 4:7, 21 _____

(2) Rom. 12:9 _____

(3) I Cor. 16:14 _____

"People need love, especially when they don't deserve it."

6 How does this love become ours?

(1) I John 4:10, 19 _____

_____

_____

(2) Rom. 5:5 _____

_____

7 Whom should Christians love?

(1) Mark 12:30 _____

(2) I Thess. 3:12 _____

(3) Luke 6:27, 28 _____

(4) Eph. 5:25, 28 _____

(5) Titus 2:3, 4 _____

8 How should love be demonstrated?

(1) I John 3:18 _____

(2) Eph. 4:2, 3 _____

_____

_____

_____

(3) I Peter 4:8, 9 _____

_____

> *"Leading health authorities have determined that the deeper cause of much illness is in the emotional reactions to life. Prolonged bitter hatred can damage the brain, and can cause heart disorders, high blood pressure and acute indigestion—all severe enough to kill a person!*
>
> *"To hate is to willfully sabotage the fine mechanism of the human body. How we all need a God-sent dose of this thing called LOVE."*
> *—Robert D. Foster*

DOING GOOD WORKS

9 For whose sake should we do good works? (Heb. 6:10)_____

10 In Titus 3:8

(1) Who is commanded to do good works? _____

_____

(2) Why should they do them? _____

_____

11 Why else should we do them?

(1) Matt. 5:16 _____

(2) Eph. 2:10 _____

_____

(3) Titus 2:14 _____

_____

_____

(4) Rev. 14:13 _____

(5) Eph. 6:8 _____

12 How does Scripture describe the lives of:

(1) Jesus (Acts 10:38) _____

(2) Dorcas (Acts 9:36) _____

_____

(3) Phoebe (Rom. 16:1,2)_____

_____

13 What are some good works God wants?

(1) I Cor. 10:24 _____

(2) I Tim. 6:18 _____

_____

"It is far better to do well than to say well."

14 Romans 12:6-21 lists over 30 good works and standards of Christian service and character. Which two or three of these do you most need

in your life? _____

_____

_____

_____

15

Other passages to consider are Matthew 25:35-40 and Christ's Sermon on the Mount, Matthew 5,6,7.

15 How are we empowered to do good?

(1) Phil. 2:13 _____

(2) John 15:4 _____

16 How should we serve?

(1) Col. 3:17 _____

_____

(2) I Cor. 10:31 _____

(3) Heb. 10:24 _____

_____

> *"Surely it ought not to be true that we, who have power with God to obtain by prayer and faith all needful grace, wisdom, and skill, should be bad servants, bad tradesmen, bad masters."*
> —*George Muller**

17 Write out Galatians 6:9, 10 in your own words. _____

_____

_____

_____

_____

_____

_____

18 What should we guard against?

(1) I John 3:17, 18 _____

_____

_____

*A. T. Pierson, *George Muller of Bristol*, Fleming H. Revell Co.

(2) James 2:15-17 _____

_____

(3) Tit. 1:16 _____

_____

THE PRACTICE OF HUMILITY

> *"Humility is perfect quietness of heart. It is never to be irritated or sore or disappointed. It is to expect nothing, to wonder at nothing that is done to me. It is to be at rest when nobody praises me, and when I am blamed and despised . . ."* —Andrew Murray

19 What was the supreme demonstration of humility? (Phil. 2:5-8)___

_____

_____

20 What does God want in His people?

(1) Micah 6:8 _____

_____

_____

(2) I Pet. 5:5 _____

_____

_____

(3) Rom. 12:3 _____

_____

_____

(4) Prov. 27:2 _____

_____

21 What does God promise?

(1) James 4:10 _____

_____

(2) Prov. 29:23 _____

_____

_____

(3) Psa. 25:9 _____

_____

22 In Luke 22:24-27, during Christ's last time with the disciples before His death

(1) What were they arguing about? _____

_____

(2) How did Jesus demonstrate His humility? _____

_____

(3) How should Christ's followers conduct themselves? (verse 27)

_____

23 In the account in Luke 14:7-11

(1) What was the evidence of pride? _____

_____

(2) What is God's principle of exalting a person? (verse 11)_____

_____

_____

24 What warnings are given us about pride?

(1) Prov. 11:2 _____

(2) Prov. 16:5 _____

18

(3) James 4:6 _____

25 Write out Philippians 2:3, 4 in your own words. _____

_____

_____

_____

_____

_____

_____

_____

> *"Humility does not consist simply in thinking cheaply of one's self, so much as in not thinking of self at all—and of Christ more and more."*
> —*Keith L. Brooks*

26 What is the best summary verse for love? _____

for good works? _____ for humility? _____

Which of these three subjects is the greatest need in your life? What

can you do about it? _____

_____

_____

_____

_____

_____

_____

_____

_____

> *"This love of which I speak is slow to lose patience—*
> *it looks for a way of being constructive.*
> *It is not possessive:*
> *It is neither anxious to impress nor does it cherish*
> *inflated ideas of its own importance.*
> *Love has good manners and does not pursue selfish*
> *advantage.*
> *It is not touchy.*
> *It does not keep account of evil or gloat over the*
> *wickedness of other people.*
> *On the contrary, it is glad with all good men when*
> *truth prevails.*
> *Love knows no limit to its endurance,*
> *no end to its trust,*
> *no fading of its hope:*
> *It can outlast anything."* —I Corinthians 13:4-7*

*J.B. Phillips, *The New Testament in Modern English,* The Macmillan Co.

Chapter Three

Developing Integrity

*"Christian character is Jesus Christ on
display in the life of the believer."*

POWER OF THE TONGUE

1 How is man's tongue described?

(1) James 3:8-10 _____

_____

_____

(2) Psalm 52:2-4 _____

_____

_____

2 What are three warnings about the tongue?

(1) Prov. 10:19 _____

_____

_____

(2) Prov. 17:9 _____

_____

(3) James 1:26 _____

_____

*"The most powerful and untameable creature in the world has its
den just back of the teeth."*

3 How does God want our tongues to be used?

(1) Isa. 50:4 _____

_____

(2) Psalm 35:28 _____

_____

(3) Psalm 145:10-12 _____

_____

_____

4 What instruction does God give about our speech?

(1) James 4:11 _____

_____

(2) Eph. 4:25 _____

_____

(3) Eph. 4:15 _____

(4) Prov. 21:23 _____

_____

_____

James 3 and Chapters 10 and 15 of Proverbs have much sound advice on the use and misuse of our tongues.

5 What does our speech reveal? (Matt. 12:34, 35) _____

_____

6 What is characteristic of the foolish person?

(1) Eccl. 10:14 _____

(2) Prov. 15:2 _____

22

(3) Prov. 29:11 _____

_____

7 What can gracious and appropriate words do?

(1) Prov. 12:25 _____

(2) Prov. 16:24 _____

_____

(3) Prov. 15:1 _____

(4) Eph. 4:29 _____

8 Review what you've learned about the tongue, and consider Psalm 141:3. In what area do you most need to pray for the Lord to guard your speech? _____

_____

_____

_____

A careless word may kindle strife,
A cruel word may wreck a life.
A bitter word may hate instill,
A brutal word may smite and kill.
A gracious word may smooth the way,
A joyous word may light the day.
A timely word may lessen stress,
A loving word may heal and bless.

HOW IMPORTANT IS PURITY?

9 What does God promise the pure in heart?

(1) Psalm 24:3-5 _____

_____

(2) Matt. 5:8 _____

10 What is God's standard for holy living? (I Pet. 1:14, 15) (Underline best answer.)

(1) Live above the standard of today's society.

(2) Follow the standards and example of other Christians.

(3) Live as holy as Christ Himself in all areas of life.

(4) Avoid being conformed to ignorant habits of conduct.

11 What is Christ's standard concerning impurity? (Matt. 5:27, 28)

_____

_____

> Sow a thought, reap an act;
> Sow an act, reap a habit;
> Sow a habit, reap a character.

12 Where do evil desires come from?

(1) Mark 7:21-23 _____

(2) Gal. 5:19 _____

13 How does God describe those who practice impurity? (Eph. 4:18,19)

_____

_____

_____

_____

14 What is God's command concerning our speech? (Eph. 5:3, 4)

_____

_____

_____

15 Why should a Christian avoid immorality?

(1) I Thess. 4:3, 7, 8 _____

_____

_____

_____

(2) I Cor. 6:15-20 _____

_____

_____

_____

(3) I John 2:15, 16 _____

_____

16 What can we do toward living a clean life pleasing to the Lord?

(1) Gal. 5:16 _____

(2) Prov. 7:1-3, 5 _____

_____

(3) Psa. 51:10 _____

(4) II Tim. 2:22 _____

_____

(5) Col. 3:5 _____

In Proverbs 7 (as in Chapters 2, 5 and 6) notice how a personal knowledge and application of God's Word is a protection against immorality.

17 What is the best summary verse on purity? _____

on avoiding impurity? _____ What are some things
that tempt your thinking away from God's standard of purity and

25

what can you do to avoid them? _____

_____

_____

_____

_____

> *"One can no more filter the mind into purity than he can compress it into calmness. To have it pure, it must be given over to the control of the Holy Spirit and the things of impurity avoided. Guard it if you would have your heart pure. Store it full of the pure truth of God's Word."* —Keith L. Brooks

WHY BE HONEST?

18 What are good goals for a Christian?

(1) II Cor. 8:21 _____

_____

(2) Luke 6:31 _____

_____

19 What should be true in all our dealings with others?

(1) Lev. 19:11 _____

(2) Lev. 25:14 _____

_____

(3) Deut. 25:13-16 _____

_____

> *"A lie is any deceit: in word, act, attitude—or silence; in deliberate exaggerations, in distortions of the truth, or in creating false impressions."*

26

20 What does God want?

(1) Zech. 8:16, 17 _____

_____

(2) Eph. 4:28 _____

_____

(3) Rom. 13:7 _____

_____

(4) Deut. 24:14, 15 _____

_____

> **Two essential standards** for a Christian are:
> —Make sure that everything you have was obtained honestly.
> —Be sure that only truth comes out of your mouth. It is not always necessary to speak, especially in matters of opinion—love, gentleness, courtesy should govern—but when you do speak, speak truth. There is no such thing as a "white" lie.

21 Where does dishonesty originate?

(1) John 8:44 _____

(2) Col. 3:9, 10 _____

> One form of dishonesty is rationalizing: "But everybody cheats on exams" or "I really put one over on the government on my income tax—saved $300—but I'll give half of it to the church."

22 What does God see?

(1) Amos 5:12 _____

_____

(2) Heb. 4:13 _____

23 What effect does dishonesty have on prayer? (Isa. 59:1-3) _____

_____

_____

24 How does Paul describe a clear conscience? (Acts 24:16) _____

_____

Did maintaining it require effort on his part? _____

_____

"Conscience does its best work only when it has been sharpened by the Word of God."

25 What did David do to maintain his honesty? (Psa. 119:29,30) _____

_____

_____

"One of the rarest powers possessed by man is the power to state a fact...To comprehend a fact in its exact length, breadth, relations and significance and to state it in language that represents it with exact fidelity are features of a mind finely balanced and singularly gifted by the Holy Spirit..." —Keith L. Brooks

Chapter Four

Growing in Discipleship

"A holy Christian life is made up
of a number of small things:
    Little words, not eloquent sermons;
    Little deeds, not miracles of battle . . .
The avoidance of little evils,
    Little inconsistencies, little weaknesses,
    Little follies and indulgences of the flesh . . .
These make up the beauty of a holy life."
                                    —*Andrew Bonar*

DILIGENCE AND DISCIPLINE

1 When does our work please the Lord? (Col. 3:23, 24) _____

_____

_____

2 In Proverbs 13:4

(1) What is the result of a lazy man's desire? _____

_____

(2) What kind of person prospers spiritually? _____

3 In how much of his work did Hezekiah prosper? (II Chron. 31:21)

_____

What caused him to prosper? _____

_____

4 What does the Bible say about a slothful person?

(1) Prov. 21:25 _____

(2) Prov. 18:9 _____

(3) Eccl. 10:18 _____

_____

"The heights by great men reached and kept
Were not attained by sudden flight,
But they, while their companions slept,
Were toiling upward in the night."

5 Consider Ephesians 5:15, 16.

(1) How does the wise Christian walk? _____

_____

(2) What should we do with our time? _____

(3) Why live like this? _____

(4) List one or two ways in which you can use your time better.

_____

_____

_____

How to make wise use of your time:

1. **Prayerful planning**—List things to be done *in order of priority.*

2. **Obedient selection**—Do the most important things first, and in faith commit unfinished ones to the Lord.

3. **Concentration and diligence**—Do the task you select wholeheartedly. Do one thing at a time and stay with it until it (or the part of it selected) is completed. Don't have a "grasshopper" mind.

"Lost, yesterday, somewhere between sunrise and sunset, two golden hours, each set with sixty diamond minutes. No reward is offered, for they are gone forever."

6 What was the result of Daniel's faithfulness? (Dan. 6:4) _____

_____

_____

7 What is required of servants of Christ and trustees of God's mysteries? (I Cor. 4:1, 2) (Underline best answer.)

(1) Zeal   (3) Dependability

(2) Ability   (4) Enthusiasm

8 In I Corinthians 9:24-27

(1) What factors are important for successfully running the Christian

race? _____

_____

(2) Is discipline connected with spiritual usefulness? _____

"A man may be consecrated, dedicated and devoted but of little value if undisciplined." —Hudson Taylor

THE PURPOSE OF SUFFERING

"Everything is needful that He sends.
Nothing is needful that He withholds."
—John Newton

9 Consider Luke 6:22, 23

(1) What are some kinds of suffering a Christian can expect? _____

_____

(2) What should be his reaction? _____

(3) What does Christ promise? _____

_____

10 In I Peter 2:20, 21

(1) What pleases God more than our patiently accepting suffering we deserve? _____

_____

(2) Why do we suffer? _____

_____

(3) What did Jesus leave us? _____

11 How did Jesus react to those who reviled Him or made Him suffer? (I Pet. 2:23) (Underline best answer.)

(1) Accused them of being unjust.

(2) Condemned His persecutors.

(3) Warned them of God's judgment.

(4) Quietly accepted their insults and persecutions.

Isaiah 52:13 through 53:12 is the great passage on Jesus as God's Suffering Servant.

12 What is one source and reason for suffering? (John 15:18, 19) _____

_____

_____

13 What are some purposes of suffering for a Christian?

(1) Heb. 12:6 _____

_____

(2) John 15:2 _____

(3) I Pet. 1:6, 7 _____

_____

_____

(4) II Thess. 1:4, 5 _____

_____

"The Gardener is always most near when He is pruning."

Hebrews 12:1-11 and the book of I Peter give much light on the promises and purposes of suffering.

14 Of what attitude and actions should we beware when we suffer? (Rom. 12:19) (Underline correct answer and complete part 4.)

(1) Complacent.   (2) Revengeful.   (3) Discouraged.

(4) Why? _____

_____

15 What attitudes toward suffering were shown by:

(1) Moses (Heb. 11:25) _____

_____

(2) Job (Job 1:20-22) _____

(3) The Apostles (Acts 5:40, 41) _____

_____

(4) Stephen (Acts 7:59, 60) _____

(5) Paul (Rom. 8:18) _____

_____

_____

"The primitive Christians knew that infinite bounty would reward their sufferings ... They were transported with joy when they were found worthy of some great humiliation; and we, lukewarm souls, we would suffer nothing; and the reason is because we lack those hopes that should support us. We sink under the lightest crosses, even under those that spring from our pride, folly or weakness." —Francois Fenelon

16 What does suffering yield?

(1) Heb. 12:11 _____

_____

(2) II Cor. 1:3, 4 _____

_____

(3) Psa. 119:67,71 _____

_____

(4) II Cor. 4:17 _____

_____

DISCOVERING GOD'S WILL

In many areas of life, God's will for the Christian is clearly stated in Scripture. In those things, doing the will of God is simply a matter of obedience. However, for other areas the Bible gives *principles* for finding God's will and guidance in decisions.

17 What promises of guidance does God give us? (Psalm 32:8) _____

_____

_____

18 What is our source of strength to do God's will? (Phil. 4:13; John

15:5) _____

_____

19 What are important conditions for finding God's will? (Rom. 12:1, 2)

_____

_____

_____

"Nine-tenths of the difficulties in finding the Lord's will are over-come when our hearts are ready to do His will, whatever it may be."

20 How do we get understanding of God's will and safe guidance?

(1) Psa. 119:105, 130 _____

(2) Psa. 37:31 _____

_____

21 What other action must we take to learn God's will? (James 1:5;

Psa. 143:8) _____

22 What did God permit in order to get the Christians to scatter through-

out Judea and Samaria with the Gospel? (Acts 8:1, 4, 5)_____

_____

23 What are other important means God uses to guide and assure us?

(1) John 16:13 _____

(2) Prov. 15:22 _____

(3) I John 3:21; Isa. 32:17 _____

(4) Psa. 84:12; Prov. 3:5, 6 _____

"Satan rushes men—God guides them."

24 You have considered the essentials for finding God's will. After the
following summaries, list the above verses that apply.

(1) Willingness, yielding to God _____

(2) God's Word _____

(3) Prayer _____

(4) Providential circumstances _____

(5) The Holy Spirit _____

35

(6) Godly counsel _____

(7) Inner peace _____

(8) Trust _____

> Sometimes God leads through just two or three of these ways, but you can be more certain of His will when you find the same leading through most of them. But be certain He will never lead you contrary to His Word.
>
> . . . more on God's will and you in **Book 6.**

Another crucial area in which the Christian needs to find God's will is that of marriage.

25 What is God's revealed will concerning marriage?

(1) Prov. 18:22 _____

_____

_____

(2) II Cor. 6:14, 15 _____

(3) Prov. 31:30 _____

_____

(4) I Cor. 7:39 _____

_____

26 What is God's will for

(1) Husbands? (Eph. 5:25, 28) _____

_____

_____

(I Pet. 3:7) _____

_____

(2) Wives? (Eph. 5:22-24) _____

_____

(Prov. 31:12, 26, 27) _____

_____

_____

27 What is God's will for all our relationships?

(1) Matt. 6:33 _____

_____

(2) I Cor. 10:31-33 _____

_____

28 Review each section of this chapter and choose a summary verse for:

Diligence _____

Suffering _____

Discovering God's will _____

How can you apply a verse from one of these subjects to your life?

_____

_____

_____

_____

_____

Chapter Five

Obedience and Blessing

"The key to usefulness, to revelation, and to a Holy Spirit filled life is obedience to the Word of God."   —*John G. Mitchell*

1   What was Jesus Christ's main concern on earth? (Heb. 10:7; John 6:38) _____

2   Consider Romans 5:19

(1) What was the result of Adam's disobedience? _____

_____

(2) What was the result of Christ's obedience? _____

_____

3   Our obedience indicates (John 14:15) (Underline correct answer.)

(1) Our sincerity in serving Christ.

(2) Our willingness to sacrifice for Him.

(3) Our love for Jesus.

(4) Our zeal for Christ's kingdom.

4   In I John 2:3, 4

(1) What does obeying the Word of God prove? _____

_____

(2) What does disobeying the Word prove? _____

_____

PROMISES AND BLESSINGS OF OBEDIENCE

5 What helps us get answers to prayer? (I John 3:22) _____

_____

_____

6 What are two results of obeying God's truth? (I Pet. 1:22) (Underline correct answers.)

(1) It makes us more fervent in His service.

(2) It helps us love other Christians.

(3) It helps us become Christian leaders.

(4) It purifies our souls.

(5) It makes us more popular Christians.

7 Even if we fail to carry them out, good intentions are to our credit. (Matt. 21:28-31)   T   F

8 To what does Jesus compare the life of a person who hears and obeys

His Word? (Matt. 7:24-27) _____

_____

_____

God is displeased with worship or attention unaccompanied by deeds. To the prophet Ezekiel He said, *"And they come unto thee as the people cometh, and they sit before thee as My people, and they hear thy words, but they will not do them: for with their mouth they show much love, but their heart goeth after their covetousness"* (Ezekiel 33:31).

9 Whom does God want to be obedient, to whom, and why?

	Who	To Whom
(1) Col. 3:20	_____	_____
Why?	_____	_____
(2) Eph. 5:22-24	_____	_____
Why?	_____	_____

(3) Heb. 13:17 _____   _____

Why? _____

_____

_____

(4) Eph. 6:5-8 _____   _____

Why? _____

_____

(5) Rom. 13:1, 2 _____   _____

Why? _____

_____

10 Are these standards frequently changed?

(1) What should a wife do if her husband is unsaved? (I Pet. 3:1)

_____

_____

_____

(2) What if a servant (or employee) has an "impossible" employer?

(I Pet. 2:18, 19) _____

_____

11 What blessings are reserved for the obedient Christian?

(1) John 15:10 _____

_____

(2) John 15:14 _____

(3) John 14:23 _____

_____

_____

(4) I John 2:5 _____

_____

_____

12 Briefly summarize the Ten Commandments. (Ex. 20:3-17)

(1) (verse 3) _____

_____

(2) (verses 4-6) _____

_____

(3) (verse 7) _____

_____

(4) (verses 8-11) _____

(5) (verse 12) _____

(6) (verse 13) _____

(7) (verse 14) _____

(8) (verse 15) _____

(9) (verse 16) _____

(10) (verse 17) _____

13 What are the two Great Commandments in the New Testament?

(Mark 12:28-31) _____

_____

_____

14 In Matthew 22:40 Jesus indicated that the Ten Commandments were summarized in the two Great Commandments.

(1) Which of the Ten are included in the First Great Commandment,

on loving God? _____

(2) Which of the Ten are included in the Second Great Commandment,

on loving others? _____

> Review "The Lordship of Christ" in **Book 2** and compare the verses under "Make Him Lord in Practice" with the Scripture in this chapter. Commands for the Christian are distributed throughout the New Testament. Watch for them as you read and study.

15 What should characterize our obedience?

(1) Psalm 40:8 _____

(2) Deut. 26:16 _____

(3) Joshua 1:7 _____

_____

16 What do Psalm 119:59, 60 teach about obeying God's Word? _____

_____

"Delayed obedience is disobedience."

17 What should be our response when God's Word seems to contradict our own judgment? (Luke 5:4,5—and notice verses 6 and 7.)

_____

EXAMPLES OF OBEDIENCE

Most of God's great servants were great in their obedience. The Old and New Testaments contain hundreds of examples. Notice the Old Testament heroes of faith and obedience listed in Hebrews 11.

18 What were two of Abraham's great acts of obedience?

(1) Gen. 12:1-4 (Heb. 11:8) _____

_____

_____

(2) Gen. 22:1-3, 9-12 _____

_____

(3) What was God's promise to Abraham's son in Genesis 26:4, 5?

_____

_____

19 What was God's remarkable commendation of David in Acts 13:22?

_____

_____

Why? _____

DANGERS OF DISOBEDIENCE

"When a Christian is in the wrong place,
His right place will be empty."

20 Consider Zechariah 7:11-14.

(1) How did the people react to God's instruction? _____

_____

_____

(2) How did it affect their prayers? _____

_____

(3) What was the result? _____

_____

_____

21 In I Samuel 15:18-23, instead of complete obedience, King Saul substituted excuses and his own way of worship.

(1) What was Samuel's reply? _____

_____

(2) To what are stubbornness and rebellion compared? _____

_____

(3) What did his disobedience cost Saul? _____

22 In what area of your life does God want greater obedience? _____

_____

When and how can you begin to "turn your feet" to God's way in this?

_____

_____

_____

_____

_____

An obedient Christian has—
A mind through which Christ thinks
A life through which Christ shows
A voice through which Christ speaks
A hand through which Christ helps.

DEFINITIONS

Adamant. . . . . Impenetrably hard; unyielding; Corundum, the hardest mineral except the diamond.

Almsdeeds. . . . . Acts of love toward others.

Apple of the eye. . . . . Pupil of the eye; something highly esteemed and guarded.

Castaway . . . . Disapproved; unusable; disqualified (A disqualified contender, one who hasn't stood the test— not one who has lost his salvation, but one who has lost his usefulness).

Chambering . . . . . . See "Debauchery" below.

Charity. . . . . God-inspired love.

Circumspectly . . . . . Carefully; cautiously; accurately.

Communicate, willing to. Eager to share and help financially.

Conversation . . . . . Behavior; conduct; manner of life.

Corrupt communication . Depraved, unwholesome, polluting or vicious talk.

Custom . . . . Taxes; tolls.

Debauchery . . . . . . Excessive indulgence of the appetites; sensuality; immorality.

Dissimulation . . . . . Hypocrisy; pretense.

Distribute, ready to . . . Liberal; generous in sharing.

Divers, Diverse . . . . . Different; a double standard (two sets of weights or measures: one for buying, one for selling).

Flesh, the . . . . Basically, human nature without God; it may also refer to cravings of self-will or sinful pleasure still present in the old nature of a Christian.

Froward . . . . Overbearing; perverse; unfair; obstinately wrong; crooked; ill-natured.

Graven image . . . . . . A carved, chiseled, or shaped image, generally made of wood, stone or metal.

Higher powers . . . . . . Government authorities — local, state, and national.

Holy Ghost. . . . . Holy Spirit; the Spirit of God.

Instruments . . . . (In Rom. 6:13) Weapons; tools.

Jesting. . . . . See "Levity."

45

Lasciviousness . . . . . See "Licentiousness" below.

Levity . . . . Flippancy; unbecoming frivolity especially in speaking of sacred or serious things; low (shady, risque or sharp) jesting.

Licentiousness. . . . . . Sensuality (gratification of the appetites of lust or gluttony); lewdness; intemperance.

Minister (verb) . . . . . . Serve.

Mortify. . . . . Put to death; deaden; deprive of power

Open face . . . . Unveiled face (see definition of this below).

Keep under . . . . Buffet; discipline; subdue.

Peculiar people . . . . . Special people; God's own people; a people for His possession.

Provoke . . . . (In Heb. 10:24) Stir up; stimulate.

Purges (verb). . . . . . . Prunes; trims; cleanses; purifies.

Quick; quickeneth. . . . Alive; makes alive.

Reckon . . . . Consider; count as true.

Revile . . . . Abusively reproach.

Rioting. . . . . (In Rom. 13:13) Reveling; carousing.

Sanctify . . . . To set apart for God's use; to cleanse from sin.

Simon . . . . Peter.

Steward . . . . Manager or supervisor of another's property; household or estate manager.

Succourer . . . . Helper.

Temptation . . . . Sometimes means a testing or trial, sometimes an enticement to sin.

Trial . . . . Difficulty; testing.

Tribute. . . . . Revenue (excise, rents, duties, taxes).

Unveiled face, with. . . . As believers in Christ (in contrast to an unbelieving Jew whose mind is veiled and prevented from seeing the truth in Christ).

Vainglory . . . . Conceit; pride; boastful stating or showing of what you are, have, or have done.

Wanteth not . . . . Lacks not.

Wantonness . . . . See "Licentiousness" above.

Your Next Step in Bible Study

Now that you have completed Book 4, you will want to go on to Book 5, *Foundations for Faith,* to learn about:

- Who is God?
- The Holy Spirit
- Sin and Victory
- Know Your Enemy
- Will Jesus Christ Return?